A LITTLE

BY MARY FLEESON

Love gives us strength to live,
it is the God-given power that
brings us closer to the divine.
Let us explore together what a
difference love makes...

Your love, Lord,

reaches to the heavens,
Your faithfulness to the skies.
Your righteousness is like the highest mountains,
Your justice like the great deep.
You, Lord, preserve both people and animals.

How priceless is your unfailing love, O God

People take refuge in the shadow of your wings.
They feast on the abundance of Your house;
You give them drink from Your river of delights.
For with You is the fountain of life;
in Your light we see light.

Psalm 36:5-9

**Try repeating the words
as you colour them in
on the opposite page.**

WHEN I SAID, 'MY FOOT IS SLIPPING,' YOUR UNFAILING LOVE, LORD, SUPPORTED ME.

Psalm 94:18

Like most people I've walked some slippery paths at times, both literally and metaphorically! I've deliberately stepped away from God and played fast and loose with the trust that God placed in me, all in the name of 'exploring' the meaning of life, the universe and everything. Really I was testing God. As a toddler will push the boundaries of their parents making, I pushed and aggravated my Heavenly Parent hoping for some tangible evidence of their existence. I wanted proof!

What I received was protection (sometimes coming from very unexpected people) and escape routes from potentially dangerous situations. Friends and family loved me unconditionally throughout. I wasn't spared the growing pains, the tears and anguish, without them I wouldn't be the person I am now, but through it all my awareness of God's love for me grew.

Think of the times your foot has slipped, give thanks to God for the people who have helped you get your balance back.

What did you learn from each stumble?

What are you still learning from the experience?

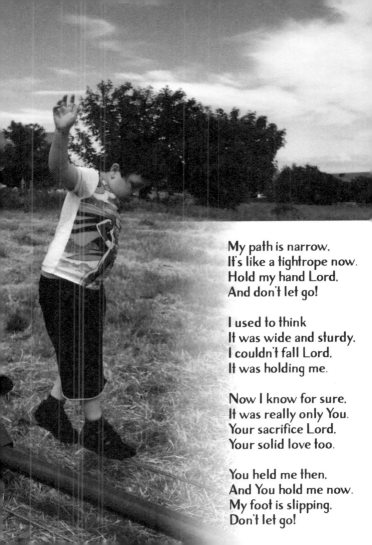

My path is narrow.
It's like a tightrope now.
Hold my hand Lord,
And don't let go!

I used to think
It was wide and sturdy.
I couldn't fall Lord,
It was holding me.

Now I know for sure,
It was really only You.
Your sacrifice Lord,
Your solid love too.

You held me then,
And You hold me now.
My foot is slipping,
Don't let go!

P As I discover more about Your Love.
    Help me to begin to understand how vast that Love is.
R As I explore my relationship with You.
    Help me to accept that Your Love is unlimited.
A As I travel further through this life.
Y Help me to rest in the knowledge of Your Love.

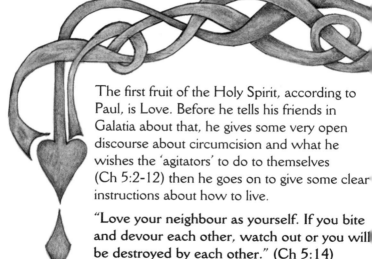

The first fruit of the Holy Spirit, according to Paul, is Love. Before he tells his friends in Galatia about that, he gives some very open discourse about circumcision and what he wishes the 'agitators' to do to themselves (Ch 5:2-12) then he goes on to give some clear instructions about how to live.

"Love your neighbour as yourself. If you bite and devour each other, watch out or you will be destroyed by each other." (Ch 5:14)

Paul didn't mince his words! The 'obvious' acts of the flesh that he casually lists ('orgies', and the like, Ch 5:19-21) weren't meant to shock but to make it clear that he not only understood human nature but that he was very aware of the temptation of instant gratification.

No one has ever seen God;
but if we love one another,
God lives in us and His love
is made complete in us.

1 John 4:12

That God may live in us and we in God,
The idea is amazing!

That I might rest, cradled in my Creator's arms,
Hold the hand that made all things,
and say, "I love You",
And hear my God say the same.

That through the wine and bread,
Love incarnate, unlimited,
I might invite God inside
And dwell in love forever.

P
R
A
Y

Loving God, I place into Your hands
the 'how' of my love for You.
Let the many ways be unlimited
as Your love is for me.

Loving God, I place into Your hands
the 'why' of my love for You.
Let the reasons be as numerous
as the birds in the sky.

Loving God, I place into Your hands
the 'when' of my love for You.
Let my love be as unrestricted by time
as You are beyond all boundaries.

What is love?

ALWAYS PATIENT AND KIND. LOVE IS NOT BOASTFUL OR CONCEITED. IT IS NEVER RUDE. AND NEVER SEEKS ITS OWN ADVANTAGE. IT DOES NOT TAKE OFFENCE OR STORE U GRIEVANCES. LOVE DOES NOT REJOICE IN WRONG DOING BUT FINDS ITS JOY IN THE TRUTH. IT ALWAYS READY TO MAKE ALLOWANCES, TO TRUST, TO HOPE AND TO ENDURE WHATEVER COMES. 1 Corinthians 13: 4 - 7

In Paul's first letter to the Christians of Corinth in Greece he spends a long time instructing, advising, challenging and encouraging the young church there. He hasn't visited for a few years and he knows of the immorality in the wealthy pagan city and the divisions that have emerged within the church. Although he aims to not diminish the message of the cross with 'wisdom and eloquence' he gave us some of the most powerful and well-known verses of the New Testament. Chapter 13 contains some of them.

1 Corinthians 13 is probably the most popular Bible passage chosen to be read at weddings, the words remind the happy couple what the foundation of marriage should be, and the congregation what the foundation of life itself should be, that love is at the root of living in community with each other and in harmony with God.

In a letter to the church in Thessalonica Paul gave this blessing.

'May the Lord make your love increase and overflow for each other and for everyone else, just as ours does for you

As you colour the outline opposite try to imagine what overflowing love could look like, how could it change our behaviour?

LET OUR LOVE OVERFLOW

1 THESSALONIANS 3:12